DIY SOLAR POWER FOR BEGINNER

The Simple Step-by-Step Practical Guide to Install Grid Tied and Off Grid Solar Power Systems for Your Home and Cut Energy Bills by 70%

by Rupert Axford

Table of Contents

Goals of this book

In this book, you will discover all you need to know to start a solar energy system for your house, from the equipment you'll need to the processes that must be taken. In this book, we will not only deliberate how to construct a solar energy system but also about the many different kinds of solar energy systems.

As a result of advancements in solar technology and the relative simplicity with which solar panels can be mass manufactured, it is now easier than ever to create electricity from the sun's innately available energy to power one's home. It is a wonderful chance to go over the fundamentals of solar power, so let's do that.

This book was written for those new to solar energy who wish to install a system to produce all of the energy their home needs from the sun. The many forms of solar energy systems, as well as the essential instruments, are discussed, along with the definition and operation of solar energy, the related rules and equations, the needed equipment, and the installation and components of a solar system.

Solar energy has several benefits, like lowering your carbon footprint and helping you save money. This book offers a more in-depth exploration of solar power by looking at the technology's inner workings. In addition, we will investigate the essential parts of a solar energy system and certain basic laws and equations, electrical circuits, and components.

Introduction

Do you feel investing in a solar power system would be good for you? For it to function, a significant number of innovative components are necessary. The information included in this book will be broken up into manageable portions for the reader. We cover everything, from the principles of solar energy up to the finer elements of setting up a house system, so you won't have to worry about missing a thing. There are now several inventions on the market that may be of assistance in lowering one's monthly expenses when it comes to bills. The technology we are going through is only one example of many. Solar power has emerged as one of the most prominent alternatives to traditional forms of energy generation in recent years. It has little influence and won't harm the environment in any way. This book is a great place to start for anybody interested in learning more about solar energy. In addition to this, the laws that control solar energy, as well as the physics that support its efficiency, will be discussed.

Renewable energy sources like solar are replacing traditional energy sources such as fossil fuels because of their higher prices. This caused a surge in the popularity of alternative energy sources. This book will discuss how solar energy works and give the foundational information required to install a system in your home. Solar energy may be used virtually in infinite ways inside the home. As a method of capturing the sun's energy, the installation of solar panels is seeing explosive growth in popularity.

The use of solar panel technology is causing a shift in the way in which individuals create and make use of power. This book will educate you on the foundations of electronics, circuits, and the many pieces of equipment you'll need to install solar panels and harness the sun's power effectively. This book discusses not just the many installation methods, including their benefits and downsides, but also the different types of solar panels and how each one operates.

CHAPTER 1
Solar energy principles

Whoever has given solar energy considerable attention has likely pondered the question of how everything works. You will be provided step-by-step instructions to operate your home on solar power. You will also be told of all of the advantages that come along with making this change. You will find the information valuable to you within these pages, regardless of whether you have already installed solar panels or are learning about solar power for the first time.

In the seventh century B.C., humans learned how to harness the sun's rays by reflecting them onto shiny surfaces to start fires. Mirrors were utilized by ancient Greeks and Romans in the third century B.C. to absorb the sun's rays, and light torches were employed in religious rituals at that time.

Edmond Becquerel, a French scientist who was just 19 years old, discovered the photovoltaic effect in 1839. At the time, he was doing research with a cell that consisted of metal electrodes that were immersed in a conducting fluid.

In 1954, two scientists working at Bell Labs, Calvin Fuller and Gerald Pearson, invented a silicon photovoltaic cell that could collect and convert sufficient amounts of solar energy to power typical home appliances. Solar panels have the potential to be used in the production of energy that may be used to power satellites, which are spacecraft that orbit the Earth.

Let's look at a few variables that have contributed to the current uptick in interest in solar power. Do you consider the process of installing solar panels to be somewhat simple? Creating power for your home using solar panels requires collecting sunlight and converting it into a form that can be used in electronic equipment. This process is known as photovoltaics. Direct current (DC) electricity must be combined with photovoltaic cells and an inverter before the energy produced by solar panels when they are exposed to sunlight can be used. Solar panels create energy when the sun shines on them. You and your home can use the power directly, or you can choose to send it into the grid so that it may be distributed to other houses in the region.

It is your choice whether or not to use a battery bank, a decision that the state of your finances will most certainly impact. Even if you cannot live completely independent of the grid, the battery bank should assist you in becoming less dependent.

Components that make up a solar cell

The process of assembling a solar panel from its components is not nearly as challenging as one may think it is. Since its beginnings in the late 1800s, solar panels have been the focus of research and development. Photovoltaic cells are responsible for transforming the direct current of the sun into the alternating current of the electrical grid. Each photovoltaic cell has a protective glass and metal shell to protect it from the environment.

Anti-reflective coatings applied to the glass that encloses silicon PV cells enable the panels to take in as much light as possible, increasing the amount of power generated by the cells. A solar inverter must be included in the system to accomplish the transformation from direct current to alternating current.

The grid

A storage facility will need to be connected to your solar power system to receive the energy that it creates. In contrast to water and gas, electricity cannot be pumped endlessly from one location to another. Either it needs to be put to use, or it needs to be moved. This is only one of the many advantages that may be gained by using a battery bank in one's house. Battery banks are necessary to store the solar energy generated by solar panels until it is required.

On the other hand, if you don't think you're ready or simply can't have a battery installed in your home, do not worry. Customers can reduce their overall energy expenses by using a "net metering" feature offered by most power providers. Solar power systems can create electricity via net metering, which enables the excess power to be sold back to the community's utility provider. As a result, the quantity of power you've given to the system may be shown on your subsequent energy account. This is a terrific approach that may assist you in maximizing your solar power system's benefits.

Remember that your family may be eligible for rebates and other financial incentives from the government and other power suppliers, even if adopting solar looks like it would be too much of a financial risk for your family's budget. In addition, there is a possibility that solar energy system installers in residential and commercial properties may be eligible for tax credits at the federal and state levels.

The company that supplies your energy may give you a one-time bill credit or a discount on the subsequent payment. Visit your local power provider's website or call them for more information about the rebates and discounts they provide their customers. On the other hand, most companies, if contacted, would be more than pleased to extol the virtues of the services they provide.

Considering the company that sells and installs your solar power system as a long-term solar partner on your property is possible. When selecting a solar partner, it is critical to collaborate with a neighborhood company with a track record of providing dependable service to its clients and making them happy.

Different panels, different features

Solar panels come in various kinds, each of which offers its advantages. Some choices may be more reasonable right now, but it's possible that they won't be there for as long as others that are a little bit more expensive.

The explanation of how solar energy works is not quite as complicated as you think. Fortunately, the process is straightforward and produces satisfactory outcomes. The sun is necessary for the creation of solar energy since the process would be impossible to carry out without it. Anything that does not get its electricity directly from the sun cannot be considered a source of solar energy since the sun is the most powerful star near us. Inverters are used to convert the electricity produced by solar panels from the kinetic energy of the sun.

Arrangements for the collection of solar energy

Solar panels, which can now be seen on roofs and in fields worldwide, have significantly influenced how we see energy and electricity. Solar farms are fields specifically designed to maximize solar energy production. Solar panels have a wide range of applications; you may use them to run a whole solar farm, or you can just utilize solar energy to power your house. You may take advantage of these good characteristics regardless of what you are attempting to accomplish.

Solar panels are a collection of individual photovoltaic cells that collaborate to turn light from the sun into usable power. However, the energy they capture must first be converted into DC electricity before it can be supplied to inverters through the electrical grid.

Inverters

In an inverter, the direct current is changed into an alternating current. So, on a day when the temperature is high, ensure that you power electrical devices with the appropriate current, which is alternating current.

Maximum distance restrictions apply when using an inverter with your home's primary electrical panel. The inverter manufacturer imposes these restrictions. In the end, the length of the wires that carry live electricity may be cut down. Therefore, before you decide where to put the inverters, you should first talk with your solar contractor about the amount of noise they make.

The circuit breaker

Your house's main circuit breaker panel may be located in the basement. Still, it might also be in the garage. In any event, this represents the trajectory of alternating current.

A fuse box, also known as a junction box, is located within your home and is responsible for regulating the flow of electricity throughout the building.

People will talk about the process of feeding additional power back into the grid using the phrase "net metering" to describe what they are doing. When you shop for a solar energy system, you will be presented with several factors: the potential amount of electricity that your solar panels can generate. You have the option of making a significant financial investment in a sufficient number of solar panels to keep your whole house operational during times of high energy demand, or you may start small and lower your monthly energy expenditures. Each of these options will help you save money. However, suppose your home's electricity is more than the amount it consumes.

Any unused electrical power will be sent back into the power grid via the fuse box in your house, which will be available for consumption by other homes and businesses. Provide your neighbors with electricity and get a credit from your energy supplier. The solar panels you have already placed will be worth more to you today than before.

You may feel comfortable even if the grid goes down for any reason, whether it be weather, a malfunction, periodic maintenance, or anything else; with today's inverter technology, you may feel secure even in these scenarios. In addition, if the electricity supply to your house is disrupted for whatever reason, you can utilize this capability, referred to as "sunlight backup," to continue operating essential devices using the power collected by your solar panels. During the installation process, your solar array will need to be set to send any extra energy it generates back into the grid during normal operation while ensuring that your home continues receiving electricity during a power outage.

Instead of maximizing the amount of electricity your solar system generates, it can be more cost-efficient to work with your solar partner to adopt net metering. Then, regardless of the circumstances, you can rely on your solar partner to guide you on the optimal next steps for your solar energy system and assist you in making the appropriate decisions at each step along the road.

CHAPTER 2
Advantages of solar systems

Investing in solar power can be a good financial decision if you live in a climate constantly hit with bad weather. Solar energy is environmentally sound and is not just for the wealthy anymore.

Powering your home with solar energy is a new technology that is gaining popularity. It is a system where homeowners install solar panels on their homes to generate electricity. The panels generate power in the daytime and use the energy to charge batteries at night. This system has many advantages over traditional energy systems:

- It is a green technology
- It saves homeowners money on electricity bills
- It is more efficient than traditional energy systems because it uses less energy to run the home than traditional systems

Solar power is becoming increasingly popular as a way to reduce environmental impact. Solar panels produce no emissions and can be installed in homes and businesses for a fraction of the cost of traditional energy sources. The panels are also easy to maintain, making them an ideal choice for those who want to save energy but don't have the time or resources to install traditional energy systems.

When you install a solar panel, you're not just saving money on electricity; you're also saving money on homes. Not only do solar panels generate energy for your home, but they also help to reduce your carbon footprint. By using solar panels, you're reducing your impact on the environment while still enjoying good quality power.

There are a variety of solar panel types and sizes that work best for you. Rooftop solar panels are typically installed in place of traditional electrical outlets. They can be used to make power for your home or business. Roof-mounted solar panels can be installed in any location, big or small, sunny or cloudy. They're also easy to maintain—just remove the panel when it becomes too tired or noisy to produce power, and replace it when needed.

If you want to place a solar panel by yourself, there are several ways to go about it. One way is to call an installer who will take care of everything from setting up the system to maintaining it. Another choice is to use one of the many online installer services available today. These services will let you choose a specific type of solar panel and installation method based on your needs and budget.

Solar panels are a reliable energy source, providing power to homes and businesses that have them installed. Solar panels work by using the sun's heat to convert it into electricity. In addition, solar panels are often easy and affordable to install, making them an ideal option for people of all ages and incomes.

Solar panels can provide power for your home or business for a long period without worrying about replacing batteries every few years. Plus, solar panels can be used in negative weather conditions, meaning you won't have to worry about going without power during extreme weather conditions.

Solar panels typically require no more than a few steps to install and keep running. For example, checking the voltage and current in each panel, replacing bulbs when necessary, and cleaning the panels can all be done without leaving your home. In addition, solar panels have low installation costs – typically around $5 per watt – so they're an excellent investment for anyone looking to save on energy costs.

Solar panels increase home value

Solar panels can increase home value by allowing homeowners to save on energy costs and increase their property values. Solar panels can be installed on a home's exterior, interior, or both. The benefits of solar panel installation vary depending on the size and location of the solar panel.

On average, a solar panel will increase your home's value by 10-15%. However, in some cases, larger panels may lead to a 30-40% increase in home value. When selecting the right solar panel for your home, there are a few things you need to consider. First, the type of solar panel you choose will affect your energy consumption and overall budget; however, the most common types include inverters and fans that allow easy connection to natural gas or electricity grids. Another important element to reflect is the size of your house—larger homes often require more powerful solar panels. In comparison, smaller homes may use less powerful panels.

Be sure to select a trustworthy installer who has experience with solar installation. Second, ensure your chosen panel system is compatible with your home's wiring and electrics. Third, follow the installer's instructions carefully - they may contain important safety information you don't want to miss. Finally, be sure to factor in your home's climate. Install solar panels may not be a good idea if it experiences significant winter or summer weather fluctuations.

Solar panels have high performance

Solar panels have many benefits when it comes to energy efficiency. For one, they are affordable and easy to install. Additionally, solar panels generate electricity even when the sun isn't shining. This means you never have to worry about running out of energy while on vacation or during a power outage.

Finally, solar panels are environment-friendly. They produce no emissions when active and don't create harmful radiation like other forms of energy generation. Solar panels also require very little maintenance – you can usually just remove them when it gets too hot or dusty outside.

CHAPTER 3

Why you should use solar energy

Despite the many benefits of solar technology, the question "Why is solar energy good?" remains. Solar energy has unquestionably triumphed as the top candidate for the position of alternative fuel source. Numerous Americans have installed solar panels on their roofs to take advantage of the numerous benefits of this kind of alternative energy.

Utilizing solar power is good for the planet

The idea that solar power generation is sustainable and environmentally friendly has gained universal support. It's possible that switching to solar energy might drastically lessen the environmental impact of human activity. Simply said, solar energy could never be considered harmful to the planet. Solar energy generation requires no additional materials beyond water and sunlight. It thus has zero impact on the global warming crisis. This means it is safe to use and has no impact on the local ecosystem. Nonetheless, the benefits of solar power are still met with some skepticism.

Using solar energy doesn't need any additional power source, and putting solar panels on your roof is a simple and low-risk way to help the environment. An easy place to start showing your awareness of environmental issues is in your own house.

One compelling argument for the further use of solar energy is the steadily falling price of solar panels. Just two examples, coal and natural gas are required to generate traditional power. These resources are not only scarce, but they also hurt the local ecology. As a direct result, energy prices will fluctuate throughout the day in an unpredictable and unstable market.

Solar panels allow you to become less reliant on the power provider. A 4 kilowatt (kW) solar system, the standard for household installations, is easy to protect yourself from growing energy bills and provides reliable, inexpensive electricity during daylight hours. In addition, energy from the sun is reliable and sustainable, and its price is fixed forever. Sun-charged batteries might be used to store energy throughout the night or on cloudy days.

Some of the advantages of solar power may still be unclear. As solar power's use increases, so do its profitability. Every country has huge swaths of completely underutilized land because they are too far from the capital city or other significant population centers to be practical.

Due to the abundance of solar energy, anybody may put land to good use and increase its value well beyond what it was previously. You may be familiar with solar farms, which are collections of solar panels spread across a wide region to store sunlight for later use.

Solar power reduces energy consumption

While power plants are responsible for generating electricity, massive networks are necessary for delivering that electricity to consumers—long-distance information transmission results in energy loss. A solar panel's function may not immediately jump out at you, but have you ever considered what it is? They have modeled their roof like yours to make the most of the sunlight. Solar panels on roofs may help improve energy efficiency by their proximity to the electrical grid. You may eliminate your reliance on the utility company and assume all responsibility for your energy use and expenditures if you generate your electricity. Due to the reliability of solar power systems, outages are less likely to occur.

Solar power increases grid security

More widespread use of solar power would reduce the frequency and severity of power outages. Every home with solar panels is effectively its little power plant in the United States. Due to these measures, our power grid will become more resilient against natural and manufactured calamities.

Subsidies for solar panels might also help you be paid for putting energy back into the grid. The use of solar energy has the potential to improve the state of our economy. The greater the uptake of solar power, the greater the need for solar panel installations by private businesses. This contributes to the economy's expansion by broadening the pool of potential consumers.

The United States, for instance, surpassed Germany as World's top market for solar photovoltaic (PV) panel installations in 2015. As a result, around 350,000 individuals in the US have found work in the solar industry.

Solar power is free

There is no way to control or hoard the sun's energy, and we get much more of it than we might ever possibly need. While the long-term savings from installing a solar energy system won't become apparent for some time, you may anticipate seeing some savings right now. You have more time to reap solar electricity's financial and environmental rewards when you save your system up and consecutively for a long time. Why? Because solar power is a sustainable option in the long run.

Solar energy has many more potential uses outside electricity production. While solar photovoltaic panels are the most common way to harness the sun's rays, this renewable resource may also be used for thermal purposes, such as keeping a home comfortable on cold winter nights.

CHAPTER 4

Basic concepts to understand

Ithe conditions inside the circuit are just right, an electric current can pass through the closed circuit. The power of a circuit and the number of electrical devices connected to the circuit can affect the amount of current that the circuit can carry at any one time. Direct current, alternating current, series circuits, and parallel circuits are all examples of electric circuits. All of the above are examples of different kinds of electrical circuits.

Acquiring a foundational knowledge of electric circuits

It is common practice to refer to each possible path taken by an electric current as a "circuit," even if this definition does not strictly apply. The charged particles responsible for the flow of electric current get their energy source from the fact that they are a component of an electric circuit. This component might be a battery, generator, or electric motor, which would be used to power various electronic gadgets.

Two basic mathematical principles may be used to characterize the behavior of electric circuits.

Understanding the power panel

Beginners will often find the easiest circuits to understand the ones that are the most straightforward and consist of the fewest number of unique components. However, the situation starts to get somewhat more difficult as soon as you include a few other factors into the mix.

It is only possible for current to flow along a single path in a series circuit, created when many resistors are connected in a chain. The fact that each resistor experiences an identical flow of electricity is another fascinating observation. In addition, the circuit's total resistance may be determined by taking the sum of the resistances of each resistor in the circuit. This is a different strategy to consider.

The concept of a circuit that operates in parallel may be understood in two distinct ways. First, one depicts the resistors' top and bottom ends being connected. Then, to calculate the overall resistance of a group of resistors that are connected in parallel, just add the reciprocals of the values of each resistor. After that, one must do the calculation necessary to determine the reciprocal of the value that was just found.

Electrical circuits may be broken down into their parts using the basic properties of voltage, current, power, and resistance. These rules explain the interdependencies between the circuit's various parameters. Ohm's and Kirchhoff's laws are named after their respective creators, Georg Ohm and Gustav Kirchhoff.

Ohm's theorem

According to Ohm's law, a circuit's voltage, current, and resistance are all inextricably linked and dependent on one another. Even though it's the simplest formula, it's the one that's employed the most often in electronics. Due to the malleability of the concept, Ohm's law may be expressed in various ways.

Calculating the current moving through the element by dividing the voltage across the resistance by the resistance itself ($I = V / R$) is possible. The amount of the electric field produced by a current may be determined by multiplying that current by the resistance of the circuit, which is the formula for calculating voltage ($V = IR$).

To calculate the resistance of a resistor, just divide the voltage across the resistor by the current flowing through it ($R = V/I$). Ohm's law may also be used to compute the power that is needed by a circuit since $P = I * V$. This is possible because $P = I * V$. It is technically possible to accomplish this goal given that the power consumption of a circuit is just the product of the current and the voltage multiplied together. Calculating the power extracted from a circuit using Ohm's law requires knowledge of two of the three variables associated with the circuit.

Either Ohm's law or the power relationship may determine the amount of heat lost by components. For example, suppose you are familiar with the particulars of your application. In that case, you may use these statistics to figure out the ideal dimensions and power ratings for the components you will use.

For instance, if a surface-mount 50-ohm resistor were to be subjected to 5 volts, the resistor would need to be able to dissipate a half watt of power. The following is an overview of the many ways that formula substitutions have evolved throughout time.

The power output is 0.5 watts, and the resistance may be either 50 or 100 ohms in both directions. For the best result, you must ensure that the resistor you pick has a power of at least 0.5 watts higher than the bare minimum. Knowing how much power the various components of a system user is useful to decide whether additional cooling or thermal considerations are required. In addition, the value of this option will decide how large the system's power supply will be.

Kirchhoff's law

Ohm's law and the concepts of Kirchhoff's circuits are integrated to provide a comprehensive theoretical framework. Kirchhoff's Current Law is concerned with energy problems, and the idea of "conservation" lies at the heart of what the law is trying to do. According to this concept, the total amount of current that flows into and out of a node (also known as a point) must be equal.

By connecting several resistors in parallel, it is possible to demonstrate Kirchhoff's current law in its most basic form. A single node in the circuit serves as the connection point for all of the circuit's resistors to the power supply. This node acts as a power collector and then sends some of the power it collects to the resistors. After that, it enables the current to flow freely away from the node and back to the point where it originated.

The alleged reduction in energy use is explained with the help of Kirchhoff's voltage law. Suppose the total voltage of the components in a circuit is not equal to zero. In that case, the circuit will not operate correctly.

You may improve upon the power supply that was just shown by connecting a large number of resistors in parallel between the supply and ground. This will ensure that each of the three circuit loops (power supply, resistance, and ground) gets the same voltage. According to Ohm's law, the voltage that is produced across a group of resistors has a relationship that is exactly proportional to the resistance value.

CHAPTER 5
How solar energy works

Solar panels are a potential source of energy generation, which opens up the possibility of using that energy to power a wide variety of electrical devices and home appliances. Solar panels have the capability of transforming the energy that is collected from the sun into a form that humans can use. Solar cells are built using alternating silicon, boron, and phosphorous layers. Silicon is an essential component. Phosphorous is the element that is responsible for the negative charge that cells have. These solar cells are the building blocks used to create solar panels at the end (which provide the positive charge). For solar panels to generate energy, they must first be able to take in photons from the surrounding environment. When photons success the superficial of the solar panel, they release energy, which, in turn, causes electrons to be expelled from their atomic orbits and into the electric field created by the solar cells. This process is known as the photoelectric effect. After this, the electric field pulls the previously trapped electrons into a current. This causes the electrons to become charged. This sequence of events is known as the "photovoltaic effect," which is also the name of the phrase used to describe it. The typical home has a roof that is significantly larger than the space necessary to accommodate the number of solar panels essential to generate the amount of solar electricity necessary to meet all of the electrical needs of the residence. This means it can meet all of the home's electrical needs with solar power. Therefore, the extra energy generated by the solar panels is sent to the main power grid. The homeowner receives reimbursement for using the grid depending on the electricity used when the house is occupied during night-time.

During the day, a home could get electricity from the grid through a solar array. This energy could then be used inside the home at night. Net metering systems allow people with solar generators that make more power than they need for their homes to make money from the extra power. Off-grid solar systems usually need a battery bank, charge controller, and inverter. The charge controller takes direct current (DC) power from the solar panel array and sends it to the battery bank as direct current (DC). The inverter changes the DC power from the battery pack into AC power that can be used by electronics that can't work with DC power. With the help of an inverter, solar panel arrays can be easily changed to meet even the most stringent needs for electricity. AC can power loads in homes, businesses, boats, RVs, remote huts and cottages, telecommunications infrastructure, oil and gas flow monitoring, RTUs and SCADAs, and many other places.

Solar panels are an efficient and cheap way to make electricity and can be used for several things. Giving up traditional utilities and moving to a home not connected to the grid is, without a doubt, the smartest thing to do. Solar energy systems may be very helpful for homes and cottages not connected to the power grid. Since this can now be done, putting up utility poles and wires from the nearest main grid access point doesn't cost as much as it used to. A solar electric system could save money over thirty years if properly cared for.

Installing solar panels gives you a lot of benefits, one of which is being able to live without the power grid. However, the fact that solar energy is renewable and good for the environment may be the most important benefit. Since global climate change started, there has been a greater sense of urgency about the work being done to reduce the effect of greenhouse gas emissions on the Earth's atmosphere. Unlike other energy generators, solar panels don't have any moving parts and need almost no maintenance. They are strong and reliable, and if they are taken care of, they could last for decades.

After the initial expenses of installation have been recouped, the remaining energy produced by solar panels and solar power is completely free for the remainder of the system's lifetime. This is the last advantage of solar panels and solar power. Contingent on how well the scheme works, this may be anywhere from 15 to 20 years in the future. There are instant advantages to be increased by installing a solar power system linked to the regional electricity grid. For instance, the owner may no longer be responsible for paying the power bill monthly; even better, the utility provider could give the owner money. These outcomes are possible by installing a solar power system linked to the regional electricity grid. How? Imagine that you have a solar electric system that enables you to generate more energy than you use in a certain period. If this is the circumstance, you may be able to sell the additional energy to the utility company serving your location. They may even offer you a higher price for it.

CHAPTER 6

How to install a solar power system on your RV

Y ou must get the installation of your solar panels right since this component of your RV is essential. But how can you choose which one is best for you? The following advice is provided to assist you in making the best-educated choice possible.

How to put solar panels on a vehicle

Solar panels are a sort of energy storage device that may be mounted on the roof of a car, truck, bicycle, or any other type of vehicle. They generate electricity by capturing the sun's rays and converting them into a usable form. Solar panels may be purchased in various shapes, sizes, and colors to meet your requirements best.

How to determine which solar panels are right for your vehicle

The number of watts a solar panel can produce will determine the panel's size. Therefore, a solar panel will need to be of a certain size, depending on the system's wattage. If the wattage is lower, the panel may be of a smaller size. Find the ideal solar panel for your recreational vehicle by speaking with a sales professional either in-person or online.

How to attach the solar panels to the vehicle

You will need to acquire tools, such as an electrical connection and a screwdriver, to attach a solar panel to your recreational vehicle. Next, take off a section of the top of your RV so you can get to the battery area. Next, take extra precautions while working near electrical cables since electric shocks or sparks that originate from the solar panels themselves might cause damage to the wires. Lastly, using the connections and screws, put the new solar panel in place.

How to cut costs when purchasing solar panels

When looking into purchasing solar panels, it is essential to perform some preliminary research. This involves acquiring knowledge of the many kinds of panels that are accessible, their characteristics, and the prices associated with purchasing them. In addition, be sure to investigate and contrast the costs of solar panels offered by various sellers. Doing your homework before investing may help you save money and guarantee that you receive the best possible bargain on that investment.

It is your duty to do comparison shopping while searching for the greatest prices on solar panels. You can locate a panel provider that meets your requirements at the most affordable price if you follow these steps. In addition, you can get a price estimate for various sizes and types of solar panels and modules if you do some comparison shopping.

When shopping for solar panels online, it may be challenging to discover affordable options when comparing different manufacturers or companies. On the other hand, using an app like Kaikai or Green Mountain Solar may assist remove the element of uncertainty when it comes to finding the greatest price on items related to solar energy. In addition, many big merchants offer things related to solar energy and other products, which means it is simple to discover everything you want without having too much of a problem experimenting with something new.

Use a solar calculator to obtain a better quote. This can assist you in determining how much solar energy you need and the kind of solar panels that will work best for your situation. Solar calculators are also available on the internet and at certain public libraries.

Before deciding on a solar panel installation, making sure the company has a Solar Panels Savings Calculator is crucial by making inquiries about it. Using this computer, you will be talented in estimating how much you will save on solar energy depending on your current living and traveling circumstances.

Installing solar panels on a recreational vehicle may help reduce the RV's monthly energy bill. You can get the ideal solar panel for your requirements if you study enough, go to various stores, and make pricing comparisons. Installing an RV's solar panels may save money and help you become more environmentally conscious. It is critical to keep this in mind since saving money is not the only benefit of doing so. You can help lessen your influence on the globe and make a difference in the environment if you follow these suggestions and put them into practice.

CHAPTER 7

How to install solar power system on a camper

S olar panels might be the most popular purchase you make for your camper. But when installing them, there are a few things to remember.

First and foremost, you'll need access to a power outlet. If your camper doesn't have one, you'll need to find an alternative way to power your solar panels. For example, heating or air conditioning may work but won't provide enough juice to operate the panels.

Next, make sure you have quality materials that will meet your expectations. For example, don't cheap out on solar panels just because they look good on paper—you want them to last as long as possible! You must also consider the weather where you plan on camping.

Solar panels are large pieces of metal placed on a camper's roof to convert sunlight into electrical energy. When used in a camper, solar panels can help power lights, appliances, and other activities while on the road.

How can solar panels be used in a camper

To use solar panels in a camper, you first need to find an appropriate location for them. You'll also want to ensure your camper has enough space to fit all the panels and mounting hardware.

First of all, select the right type of solar panel for your camper – whether you're looking for cheaper or more expensive panels. Cheap solar panels may not generate as much power as more expensive ones so they won't last as long. Additionally, cheap solar panels may not function as efficiently as more costly panels. Finally, ensure that your camper has an adequately sized roof rack to store the panels. Otherwise, you may have difficulties mounting the panels properly.

Installing solar panels in a camper

When it originates to installing solar panels in a camper, it's important to have some basic skills and knowledge. However, you don't need to be experienced with wiring or installation to do this process; just follow the steps drawn below, and you must be able to install solar panels successfully.

First, take off your camper's top cover and remove any obstructions from view inside the camper, such as cords or batteries that could be hindering panel installation. Next, connect each panel wirelessly using an appropriate surge protector (or an unplugged electrical outlet). Once all wires are connected properly, replace the top cover and reattach any obstructions inside the camper. Finally, turn on your electrician, who will help connect your PV modules using waterproof connectors.

To get the greatest out of your astral panels in a camper, it's important to have a comprehensive understanding of how they work and what types of connectors are needed to connect them. In addition, it's also important to be familiar with the installation instructions the installer provides. By reading this chapter and following the steps outlined therein, you should be able to install solar panels successfully in your camper.

Solar panels in a camper should be chosen carefully based on the specific needs of your camper. For example, using a caravan as your primary travel vehicle, use UV-resistant and waterproof panels that can handle wet weather. If you'll be using your camper on vacation, opt for LED or high-efficiency windows that can save power and reduce noise.

Choose the right solar panels for your camper

Choosing the right solar panel is important because it will determine how much power your caravan will generate and how much money you'll spend on electricity each month. Factors to consider include wattage (how many watts of power a panel produces), efficiency (how well a panel converts sunlight into electrical energy), and color (which colors are best suited for outdoor use).

Be sure to ask about warranty service and whether any kind of discount is available for those who purchase multiple panels from the same company.

Once you've learned how to set up and use solar panels properly, move on to thicker or more powerful panels to increase battery life or larger arrays for better performance over time.

Solar windows may be used in many ways to power your camper and boost efficiency. But there are a few things you need to think about before you set them up. Start with solar panels in a camper right now by picking the correct ones for your vehicle.

CHAPTER 8

How to install solar power system on your boat

For many boaters, solar panels answer their boat battery needs. In addition, solar arrays on boats can offer a variety of benefits. Still, there is an insufficient belonging you should keep in mind when choosing a solar panel system for your boat.

Solar panels for boats can provide several benefits, including reducing energy costs, saving water usage, and improving the environment. Here are some key opinions to consider when selecting a solar panel system for your boat:

- Solar panels should be installed on the boat's top. The panels should be placed in an optimal location for shading and protection from the sun while allowing full use of the boat's electrical system
- Panels installed on top of a boat may have better views and less sunlight
- Consult with your local boating store before making any purchases to ensure you get the best solar panel system for your needs

How to select the correct solar panel for your boat

There are several different types of solar panels for boats. Here are a few examples:

- Panels that use metal plates to convert sunlight into electrical energy. These panels can be mounted on the roof or below the boat and last many years without replacement.
- Panels that use plastic tiles to convert sunlight into electrical energy. These panels can be mounted on the boat directly or in between decks and typically last much longer than metal panels.

Your boat may have different needs when it comes to solar panel compatibility. For example, some boats need more wattage than others, so you'll need to choose a panel with a higher wattage rating to generate enough electricity for your boat. Conversely, other boats may not require as many watts of power, so you'll want to find a panel with lower wattage ratings to save money.

Get a quote for a solar panel for your boat

To get a quote for solar panel installation, contact one of several commercial solar companies that offer quotes online or over the phone. Be sure to ask about specific boat measurements and needs to get the best quote possible.

Tips for successfully installing a solar panel on your boat

Solar panels are a great way to save money on your boat. Using them correctly can reduce costs and make your voyage more affordable.

To get started, consult a solar installer to find the right system for your boat. Then, choose a panel that is compatible with your particular vessel and design, as well as one that is efficient and reliable. Factors to consider when choosing a solar panel include the location of the panel on your boat, how much power you need to generate, and what type of environment you'll be sailing in.

Remember that not every spot on your boat will be compatible with a solar panel, so it's important to research each installation before buying one. You can also discover online calculators to assist you to choose an effective solar panel for your specific needs. One of the greatest significant things you can do when installing a solar panel on your boat is to keep it clean. By keeping any stray cords and wires from becoming tangled up in theolin array, you'll be sure to have trouble neither damaging nor operating your boat without solar panels.

CHAPTER 9

How to install a solar power system on your cabin

W hether building your first cabin or remodeling an old one, this guide will help you get the job done right. From choosing the right solar panel type to keeping your panels clean and healthy, we've got you covered.

Why solar panels are awesome for cabinetry

Solar panels are neat pieces of equipment that can be installed on the roof of a building to harness the sun's rays and provide electricity for electronics and appliances inside. Not only may solar panels save energy costs, but they also provide a stylish touch to your home.

Panels that absorb sunlight may then be used to generate electricity for electronics. Then all you have to do is ascribe solar panels to the roof of your house or building and plug them into an electricity outlet. They are simple to erect and dismantle, guaranteeing that you will never be without a reliable, clean power source. In addition, they are stylish and functional, making them ideal for any contemporary interior.

How to do it right when installing a solar panel on a cabin

Choosing the right solar panel is important when installing a solar panel in a cabin. First, you need to choose a device that will fit into the space available in your cabin and produce enough power to light up your cabin during the day. Solar panels come in many sizes, shapes, and colors to meet your needs.

Mount the solar panel

Mounting the solar panel is an important part of installing it in a cabin. Ensure the solar panel is level, placed properly in other parts of your cabin, and connected to the electricity supply. You can also use bolts or nails to hold the solar panel.

Connect the solar panel to the cabin electricity supply

Connecting the solar panel to the cabin electricity supply is another important step when installing it. Brand sure you consume an electrical outlet close to plug in the solar panel and power up your cabin. You can also use a surge protector if you want to keep some power going while not using all of the energy from the solar panel at once.

Use the solar panel to power the cabin

If you want to use the solar panel to power your cabin, make sure that you turn it on and off regularly. You can also use it to light up your cabin at night. To do this, connect the solar panel directly to the power outlet in your cabin and turn it on or off as needed.

When installing a solar panel in a cabin, it is important to use a stud to secure the panel to the cabin floor. Then, use a ground wire to connect the panel to the electrical system and avoid damage to the panel or surrounding area by using a shield.

Solar panels can be a great addition to any cabin. You can get the most out of your investment by choosing the right solar panel and mount. With all of these subjects in mind, it's important to ensure that your solar panel installation is done correctly so that your cabin remains safe and tax-deductible.

CHAPTER 10

Important tools to install a solar energy system in your home

Being a homeowner requires you to do a certain amount of maintenance work, which is the kind of labor that a handyperson would be able to undertake. If you have the appropriate tools, you should be able to repair typical problems in your houses, such as leaky faucets, misaligned cabinets, and jammed doors and windows. On the other hand, suppose you're feeling courageous and have a solid knowledge of the concepts at play. In that case, you may even be able to tackle more extensive repairs on your own.

I have produced a list of the most crucial pieces of equipment you should have on hand as if the process of moving into a new house wasn't already stressful enough.

Screwdrivers

Suppose you ever find yourself needing repairs around the home. In that case, you should ensure that you have both a head screwdriver and a flat head screwdriver (also known as a cross-slot screwdriver) on hand at all times. The screwdriver bases found in most home improvement and hardware stores are intended to be compatible with a diverse selection of screwdriver heads. One of the best applications for these tools is to loosen and retighten screws.

Hammer

The task may easily be accomplished using a simple clawed hammer with a round head. Picks with a weight in the middle range often feature a rip claw, used to pry out nails. Replace your wooden handle with one made of metal or fiberglass instead of continuing to use the one you have. In addition, a mallet hammer is an important item to have on hand for any little demolition work you may need.

Hammers with claws are useful for driving nails into wood and extracting them from the substance. This is one of the many situations in which this occurs. Even though they may be used for demolition, a mallet hammer will give you more accuracy for working with things that need to be demolished.

Wrenches

Several types of wrenches must be used, including an allen wrench, an open-end wrench, a mixture wrench, an adaptable wrench, and a socket wrench.

Each kind of wrench is well suited for a certain task. For example, when putting together pieces of furniture for the home, an Allen wrench is a typical tool used for tightening and loosening nuts and bolts. On the other hand, you might get a large assortment of wrenches to assist you with various jobs. An adjustable wrench, often called a crescent wrench, is one of the most helpful instruments. Because of its adaptability, it may be used in various contexts and with various nuts and bolts.

Pliers

Pliers with cutting edges, needle-nose pliers, and slip-joint pliers are all critical tools that should be included in the toolbox of every electrician. These pliers may cut the wire and grab, tighten, and unhook various metal components.

Knifes

Although you may buy retractable and folding utility knives, they are the same product. The only change is in the way they are stored.

Because of the sharp blade of a utility knife, it is well suited for precision cutting, making it an important tool for any job involving home renovation. In addition, this procedure is safer since it often only requires one cut to be done instead of several cuts using a dull knife or scissors.

Measure tape

There are a few distinct varieties of measure tape, each of which may be differentiated from the others based on their construction. Most undertakings involving house repairs need the utilization of a metal tape measure capable of being looped back on itself. You might use a cheaper plastic that won't last as long but will save you some money. This will make things more difficult for you if you are the one measuring independently.

Level

Even though there are over twenty distinct types of levels, most houses just need a carpenter's level. In addition, you have choices for the length and the kind of cloth (wood, plastic, or aluminum are all options).

Check that everything is exactly aligned in both the horizontal and the vertical directions. For example, if you want to prevent a shelf from tilting while mounting it to the wall, you should use a level.

Stud finder

You should be able to get away with a pretty basic model, even if there are multiple variants. Of course, we are speaking specifically about an electronic stud finder when we say this.

By locating the wooden and metal studs behind the walls with the help of a stud finder, it is possible to get insight into what is going on behind the walls. Some recent devices may even provide an audible warning sound if they identify a certain kind of wire. Additional support from a wall stud is required when hanging large things on the wall. As a result, having these details close to hand is beneficial.

Flashlight

If you want to get anything done around the house while it's dark outside, you'll need a flashlight far more powerful than the one with your phone. It is better to use a headlamp than a small or medium-sized LED flashlight if you do not want the hassle of holding or aiming the flashlight.

Electric drills

The versatility offered by a cordless 12-volt drill cannot be matched by any of the other variations of electric drills now on the market. This tool may create holes in walls and other surfaces, regardless of whether one is doing maintenance or starting from scratch.

Duct tape

It is recommended that you use a standard roll of duct tape. However, if you want, you are free to experiment with various colors and designs.

In all honesty, we should ask, "What can't be fixed with duct tape?" Because it may be used in various ways, it is justifiably considered one of the home's most significant products. It is best to avoid putting the glue in places that might be exposed to high temperatures since doing so would diminish the efficacy of the adhesive.

Screws

Because there is such a wide variety of sizes and styles available for both nails and screws, it is a good idea to have a selection of both in stock at all times. In addition, drywall installation requires various nails, including finishing nails, galvanized nails, vinyl nails, anchors, and screws. Therefore, we need a centralized place where most of their requirements may be satisfied.

In various circumstances, you may use them to secure objects to walls and other types of flat surfaces. In the same job, you may use nails and screws interchangeably, even though both types of fasteners have various sizes.

CHAPTER 11
Different kinds of systems and components

The question "What components do I need to finish my solar power project?" is one of the most common worries people are just starting to work on solar power projects at home. Follow the example of many do-it-yourself solar power systems, which often improve their photovoltaic systems by utilizing used components bought online. As a consequence, you may be able to save money on solar energy.

Before you begin making purchases or assembling the various component components on your roof, you should first receive a high-quality solar guide that will walk you through the entire process of designing, installing, and customizing your own home solar energy system. This should be done before you begin assembling the various components. As a direct consequence, the likelihood of you committing any errors as you go forward has decreased. Let's look at the seven components of your solar power system that are necessary for it to function, in addition to time, equipment, and instructions. These components are listed in descending order of importance.

A solar power system that can be connected to the grid is comprised of seven primary components. These components need to be wired together in a certain order to work effectively.

Solar-powered batteries

Most photovoltaic solar panels used in residential installations and do-it-yourself solar power systems are constructed by the homeowner using materials already lying about the house. On the other hand, low-cost photovoltaic cells may be ordered online and combined into solar panels with a power output of 80W, 100W, or 120W.

Suppose you do not have the time or skill to make your solar panels. In that case, there are several commercially available options that you may choose from. The greater the size of the solar array, the greater the number of panels that need to be connected.

You will need deep-cycle batteries to keep the lights on through the night and store the additional energy that your solar panels create. A shallow-charge battery has a lead plate that is less thick than standard batteries since it was developed especially for use in automobiles. On the other hand, the lead plate inside a deep-cycle battery is much larger.

Deep-cycle storage batteries can be charged and discharged many times than standard batteries, which is one reason solar systems that utilize these batteries have a longer lifespan than those that use standard batteries. Therefore, it is more cost-effective to purchase used deep-cycle batteries than brand-new ones. In addition, there is a possibility that you might save costs by recycling used batteries from electric forklifts or golf carts.

Batteries store energy for later use, such as when the system is not generating power, but the energy is still required. One example of this scenario is after the sun has set, but the energy is still needed. Customers who make most of their energy use at night find that battery technology is becoming an increasingly attractive choice. Electricity is required twenty-four hours a day, seven days a week.

Since the battery sector is still in its infancy, even though battery technology has made significant advances in recent years, it stands to reason that battery prices will remain relatively high. The addition of batteries to your solar energy system may or may not increase its value depending on factors such as the feed-in tariff rate and the purpose for which the batteries will be used. The money you will get from the government is known as the feed-in tariff, and it is given to you if you connect your energy output to the grid for broad consumption. You will not receive payment for the energy stored in batteries because it will not be returned to the grid. Suppose your FIT rate is high, and you aren't utilizing the energy you create because you aren't at home or work during the necessary hours. In that case, storing energy isn't a cost-effective solution to your energy needs.

Disconnects

Even though it is nothing more than an electrical switch, every solar power system requires a disconnect, which is a component that must be present. For example, suppose a problem or routine maintenance is required. In that case, your solar panels and array's direct current power output may be turned off. Therefore, this disconnect switch has to restrict the total amount of electricity generated from the solar panels even when the sun shines brilliantly.

Remote controller

Most household solar power systems feature backup batteries, used when the sun is not shining, such as overcast or dark outdoors. The battery charge controller is responsible for determining how fully charged each battery is. Because of this, the batteries won't be overcharged, and the backup batteries won't be drained into the system all through the night. In addition, it won't break the bank to replace this component because it functions similarly to the battery charger in your automobile.

Measurement and analysis of power across the whole system

It is not needed to install a solar power meter, but doing so is strongly suggested so that you can carefully interpret the amount of free energy that is being created by your solar panels. In addition, solar power meters assist you and your neighbors in optimizing your solar system so that you may realize the greatest possible financial savings. This is accomplished by exchanging information on the amount of money saved by your neighbors as a direct result of your solar system.

Transformers

While the mains provide alternating current (AC), the solar panels on your roof create a direct current. Your home is wired to receive power from the mains (DC). To convert the direct current (DC) energy that your photovoltaic panels produce into the alternating current (AC) power that your house uses, which is either 115, 220, or 240 volts, you will need a solar power inverter.

With the help of an inverter, the wall outlets of your solar panels can accommodate virtually any appliance powered by a conventional electrical outlet, including electric drills, laptops, vacuum cleaners, and even mains-powered appliances. You can then use the sun's energy to power these devices directly. Inverters that produce square waves or modified sine waves are common. Still, a high-quality 1200W sine wave inverter can currently be obtained for less than a few hundred dollars.

Easily reachable batteries

When the sun isn't shining, and the storage batteries are running low, you may have no choice but to use the backup power. The majority of systems now come equipped with backup generators as standard equipment. The diesel generator is the most frequently used as a stand-alone power source. The grid-tied inverter allows the system to draw backup power from the utility grid when necessary. In this scenario, generating electricity from renewable sources such as wind turbines and small hydropower systems are two examples of potential applications for this kind of technology.

It is less difficult to utilize solar energy to power your home than you may imagine, regardless of whether you want to build your solar panels from scratch or acquire panels that have already been built for commercial use. You can get started using solar energy now. Having a system linked to the grid also allows you to recover some of the money you have spent on energy over time by selling any excess power that you produce back to the utility.

Solar panels are just one constituent of a solar power system, which should surprise anybody. A wide selection of brand names is available for each system component. The performance of a system is strongly reliant on the quality of the components that make up that system, and the goods that these firms make have the potential to make or break that performance. Given this, it's not surprising that many individuals are reluctant to make solar energy their major power source. I hope that this chapter will be a useful resource not only for those who are new to the idea of home energy systems but also for those who already have one installed in their home by helping them better understand the various parts that make up the system and how they work together to provide power to the home.

Solar power systems are typically composed of four primary components: the panels, the inverter, the rack, and the batteries.

Panels

Since solar panels are your system's most visible component, it is reasonable to assume that you have the greatest expertise in managing and maintaining them. If you take a fast walk around the neighborhood right now, you should be able to determine which homes in your neighborhood have solar panels and which do not.

Solar panels are made up of individual solar cells, which are responsible for converting sunlight into useable direct current (DC). When solar cells are placed under direct sunlight, the flow of electrons within the cells begins to become increasingly rapid and efficient. Solar panels, responsible for generating electricity, are powered not by the sun's heat but by kinetic energy. It's possible that overheating a panel will have the same impact as overheating a computer, which will reduce the device's efficiency. Suppose you want to ensure that your investment in solar energy will remain viable for at least 25 years. In that case, the solar panels you buy should have the capacity to withstand the high temperatures typical in some areas of the US. Because there is such a wide variety of solar panels, it may be challenging to choose where to start looking for them. Let's take a rapid look at the skills and products available to you before we go further into these issues in the next chapter.

In terms of their technological capabilities, which kind of panel, polycrystalline or monocrystalline, is more advantageous? Monocrystalline panels are simple to identify since they do not have cell corners. This is because the production process produces a single enormous crystal at the end of the product. As a result, the color of a monocrystalline panel is often darker, and the look of the panel might vary from one panel to the next.

In polycrystalline panels, it is possible to discover both light and dark blue crystals, with some sections having a blue coloration closer to a pastel than others.

Since the commencement of the solar business in the US, monocrystalline panels have had a widespread reputation as being at the technical front of the industry. Because larger crystal sizes have a stronger tendency to have a better absorption capacity, monocrystalline solar cells have historically had higher peak efficiencies than polycrystalline solar cells throughout solar cell history. However, after a large amount of time has elapsed, the advantages one technology has over another have, in many instances, diminished to the point that they are practically irrelevant. Because of its pleasant year-round temperature range, the US is an excellent place for installing solar panels of either monocrystalline or polycrystalline.

The length of time the product will remain useful, the reliability of the manufacturer, and the efficiency with which the product will perform its intended function are all aspects that need more examination. However, in and of itself, each of these three factors can be the deciding factor in establishing whether or not you can cut down on your overall energy consumption, increase your return on investment, and get assistance if anything goes wrong.

Choosing and buying the best solar panel for your home

When it comes to solar panels, much like many other aspects of life, the more money you invest in them initially, the better off you will be in the long run.

Low-cost panels may seem appealing at first, but in the long term, they often deteriorate more quickly and have less impact. Either that or they are completely ineffective. So, stay away from it unless you want your life to explode. When considering the system as an investment for the long term, it is important to keep in mind the system's effectiveness, the caliber of the installation, the anticipated lifespan of the components, and the warranties offered by the system. Instead of focusing on immediate expenses, one of the most effective tactics is to look forward to potential cost reductions in the long run. Many companies provide their customers with low-quality goods at a reduced cost to maintain their competitive pricing positions in the marketplace. This leads to hasty installations, which puts your property at risk, and the selling of materials that won't survive more than five years if placed on an American roof. A fundamental quality and performance warranty that extends over the first 20–30 years of usage is included with every single one of our products.

As we have already seen, every solar power setup has to include an inverter as one of its components. The power shaped by your solar panels at 240 volts direct current (DC) is converted by these components into electricity at 240 volts alternating current (AC) so that the electrical appliances in your house may use it. Because it is always running, the inverter has a greater risk of failing than any of the other components of your solar energy system. This suggests that they often come with a warranty that is valid for a length of at least ten years. Because of this, it is generally suggested that you select an inverter of good quality manufactured by a firm like Fronius, ABB, Sun Grow, or SolarEdge.

String inverter vs. microinverter

Microinverters and string inverters are the sorts of inverters that are used most often; however, there are numerous more forms. It is necessary to situate a string inverter in a location that is shaded to convert the direct current (DC) power that is generated by a string of solar panels (often the whole system in residential systems) into alternating current (AC). A microinverter is attached to the back of each solar panel. Because each solar panel has a microinverter, it can function independently from the others. There is a possibility that the output of an entire string inverter system might be negatively impacted by the partial shading of a single solar panel. Microinverters have made it possible for solar panels to function on their own, which means the issue may finally be resolved. However, the addition of those things will cause the prices to go up. Power optimizers are an option that falls somewhere in the middle of these two categories; they are less efficient than microinverters but cost less money. Because shading isn't always an issue, microinverters aren't often required in most situations.

Racking

Racking, often known as the installation procedure, is one of the essential components of a solar power system. Utilizing this component won't have to worry about your solar panels slipping off the roof.

Many companies place a higher priority on speed than either the happiness of their customers or the safety of their property while installing the product. Installers who operate at a large volume for low salaries and who lack the requisite skills are often accused of cutting shortcuts, leaving holes in roofs, and not properly attaching live wires. This accusation is common since these installers lack the essential qualifications. In addition, they have a well-deserved reputation for making hasty choices.

CHAPTER 12
Power generation from solar energy

The installation of solar panels is a significant issue, so let's get started on that right now. Depending on your supplies, you can hire a professional EPC installation service or do the task independently. This chapter will walk you through the process of putting up your own solar power system from the ground. If you read this chapter, you could learn enough to put solar panels on your roof if you do it all by yourself. In the past, some thought was given to installing a solar array with a power output of one kilowatt. The installation of solar panels involves a significant amount of prior preparation and thought. Because it does not make a difference where the panel is placed, the installation process cannot be left to chance. It is essential to position them in a way that will allow them to have the possible effect and provide you with the greatest possible return on your investment. The sun is the primary energy source for photovoltaic panels, which are required to convert solar energy into usable electricity. The sun moves across the sky daily, never staying in one location for more than a short time. As a result, it is imperative that while installing solar panels, consideration be given to the path taken by the sun during the day.

The rooftop of a building is where one will most often see solar panel installations. At this point, the sun's rays first make contact with the building. It is also the point at which they are most likely to remain for the whole day, given that the roof of the structure seldom causes the beams of light from different sources to interfere. Solar panels may be fastened to the surface of a roof in one of two methods. Either solar panels may be affixed to the peak of an already-existing roof, or the whole roof can be swapped out with one covered in solar panels.

The first method of installation is the one that is used most often. It is simple, and carrying it out won't result in any more hassle or expense on your part. The underlying contrasts between the two approaches are highlighted by the fact that the second method requires much more time to complete. Even though it will be more expensive and take more time to implement, it could be the best choice in the long run. Getting the object in the correct location is the most important aspect of any technique. A general method can accomplish this goal regardless of the technique used. For example, most solar panels are affixed to the south-facing slope of a roof since this orientation allows for the most solar energy output.

It is essential to ensure that the area where your solar panels will be installed is large enough to satisfy all your current and future requirements for electrical power. Getting your solar panels installed in the best possible location is a separate challenge. Solar panels are not the optimal choice when considering factors such as cost-effectiveness, size, and amount of electricity produced. If your power requirements are far higher than normal, you will need a significantly more resilient array.

The work is recommended to be given to qualified professionals with experience installing solar panels. They have experienced all there is to experience and are prepared to handle any problem. Before deciding to install solar panels, it is important to consider the amount of sunlight your region receives every year, the force of the damaging winds that are likely to occur, and the potential energy output of the ideal location for putting solar panels.

Components essential to a proper solar panel setup

Switching to solar energy is a straightforward and cost-effective way to reduce your impact on the environment and save money on your monthly electricity bill. Installing solar panels may be a straightforward and low-cost job, but this is only the case if thorough thought and attention are given to every aspect of the endeavor. You may reduce the likelihood that your household's solar update will become a significant source of stress.

First of all, you need to give some thought to how much time and money will be required of you to choose a solar system and have solar panels installed. To put this another way, the typical cost of installing a solar power system on a home with a low need for electricity is around $9 for every watt generated. Because of this, you will learn that this is an expensive endeavor, even if the amount of electricity you use is little.

In the Pacific Northwest, hydroelectric power is a renewable energy source, and the electricity cost in this section of the country is often less expensive than in other parts. The high cost of installing solar panels much outweighs the benefits that would be gained from doing so.

Fundamental components of solar panel setup

After determining the electricity, your house requires. Whether or not the accompanying expenditures would be too much for you to handle, you can go forward with installing your solar panels.

Installing solar panels is not a straightforward task that can be finished in a single weekend because of the complexity of the electrical infrastructure that lies underneath the panels themselves. In addition, before commencing installation, you must ensure that you have obtained the necessary licenses from the appropriate authorities in your region. If you want to keep track of how far along the installation process is, you may need to hire a contractor or at least arrange for regular inspections.

As for the panels themselves, they should be positioned on your roof at a 45-degree angle, with the south-facing side looking down towards your house. This will maximize the sunlight that enters your home via the panels. This will allow the most amount of natural light possible into your house. The southerly direction is best for plants since this is the direction in which they will get the most constant amount of sunshine. A northern exposure in the winter results in low absorption because of the lack of sunlight.

You will need batteries and a generator for your home if and only if you ever want to cut it off from the local electrical grid completely. Installing a backup generator is recommended to complement the amount of power produced by your solar panels. When the sun isn't shining, the energy in your home comes from a backup battery system.

When it comes to safeguarding that an electrical system continues to work properly, the remaining components perform an important role as safety precautions, which is why they are left out of the sentence. By maintaining a constant check on the amount of power that is being extracted from the battery, the charge supervisor protects the battery from getting overcharged. If you have an inverter, you can use the energy your solar panels produce inside your home's outlets.

The price of converting solar energy into usable power may change quite a bit, depending on the size of the solar panels. The cost of the panel rises proportionately with the size of the panel purchased.

Installation options might include flush mounting to walls or ceilings, poles, roof brackets, and roof brackets. Roof brackets are also an option. During the installation process, you will get instructions that will enable you to finish the task without any more help from the installers. Before installing solar panels, one must understand how each of the three mounting choices (pole, roof mount, and flush) works. This is because each option affects how the panels are positioned relative to the sun.

Poles and flush mounts support each panel, and flush mounts are also utilized to assist in installing the panels on the roof of the building. Alternatively, you may install your system on the ground or the roof by using roof or ground mounts. When the mounts are used, the panels are fastened into position with much more steadiness than is otherwise possible.

Solar panels must have north-facing sides facing south to produce the most usable electricity. In addition, you need to clear the area around the solar panel of anything that could be blocking the sun's rays so that they can light straight on the panel. The training sessions devote significant time to thoroughly covering each topic. A small angle must be applied in the latitude direction to ensure that each panel receives the necessary sunshine. You'll also note that the panel needs some maintenance from time to time as you use it. As a consequence of this, the correct functioning of the panel is dependent on the instruction that you get.

Despite this, you should have them installed because of the advantages they will provide you in the long run. Assuming the panels are kept in excellent condition following the installation, you will only have to pay the initial cost of purchasing them once. In addition to these advantages, using solar panels is also beneficial to the environment since it is simple to run. As a result, it is feasible from a financial perspective, even though it could occasionally need maintenance to perform adequately. If you take the time to learn how to install it yourself, you might save money on the labor charges associated with doing so.

It shouldn't be difficult to install solar panels on your roof if you have the necessary information and are well prepared. In addition, it is essential to be ready by training well using the many methods available.

In recent years, there has been an increase in the popularity of placing solar panels on residential buildings due to the many financial and environmental benefits associated with doing so. Solar panels are equipped with photovoltaic cells responsible for converting the energy from the sun's rays into a usable form. This power source may also help operate heaters and other electrical devices. The generated power may either be immediately sent to the devices, or it can be stored in a battery for use at an advanced time. However, the process of installing it could be complicated. Still, it isn't impossible if you have the right tools and an understanding of electrical systems' functions.

Costs

These variables will significantly impact the total cost of constructing the panel system. For example, an individual solar panel with a power output of 75 watts typically costs close to $900 when bought separately. A panel with a capacity of 2 kilowatts often costs in the range of $16,000 to $20,000. In comparison, a system with a capacity of 5 kilowatts typically costs $30,000 to $40,000.

Solar panels installed on buildings are the most common and efficient way to collect sunlight to generate electricity. Additionally, if there is sufficient space, they might be built as distinct structures near the primary structure. You have the choice of putting your solar panels in one of three distinct ways: flush, on the roof, or the ground. Roof installations must have a flush mount to remove any potential visual impediments. Roof-ground mounts connect solar panels to a flat surface such as a roof or the ground, whereas pole mounts are used to secure solar panels to a single pole. Pole mounts may also be used to secure solar panels to many poles.

The panel has to be oriented to face the sun for the solar energy generation to be at its maximum. It is impossible to throw away sunlight by blocking its path with obstructions.

For example, in latitudes ranging from 0 to 15 degrees, the highest panel tilt permitted is 15 degrees, and the angle at which each panel is slanted has to be the same. Following the completion of the repair, the solar panel has to be examined to guarantee that it has been correctly sealed and that no light will leak out. The panel must then be connected to a battery-powered inverter or an electrical junction box to continue functioning.

Methods and suggestions for the installation of solar panels

Suppose you put a renewable energy source on your property, such as solar panels. In that case, you may want to conceal them as much as possible to avoid drawing attention to them. However, rooftops are often used as installation sites because of their accessibility and sense of security. In addition, there are other things you may do, such as making better use of portions of your yard that are currently being underutilized.

Solar power production is only possible in areas with adequate sunshine at the site where the panels will be put. As a result, this is yet another prominent argument in favor of placing solar panels on the roof of a building.

Another challenging aspect of the installation is working out how to link up all of your panels. If it is to be mounted so that it lies horizontally on the ground or the ceiling, a mounting mechanism is required. Consider whether or not you will need to tilt your solar panel to make the most of the energy it produces. If at all feasible, you should arrange for replacing your roof to coincide with the installation of solar mounts on your roof simultaneously. This flash could solve the leakage problem that your solar mounting system is having.

Mounting the solar panels, constructing the panels themselves, and ultimately connecting them to the power inverter are the three steps that make up the traditional method for installing solar panels. Always ensure that the mounts are put in a straight line across the wall. The roof mounts will be attached to the rafters throughout the structure. Utilizing a stud finder is one method that may be used to locate the rafters in the ceiling. Next, several fasteners may attach solar panels to the rails that protrude from the mounting. After completing that step, the panels may be assembled into a bigger structure by connecting them.

The first step in installing solar panels on the home's roof has been taken. In most configurations, just a portion of the inverter is shielded. The direct current (DC) electricity produced by the solar panels is changed by the inverter into alternating current (AC) power so that it may be used inside the home. In most instances, an inverter will be physically connected to the electrical grid to keep the voltage and frequency stable.

You may contact the local government to determine whether the companies that serve your utilities will buy back any excess power your home generates. Despite this, it is essential to have your solar panels hardwired into the grid so that you continue to have access to energy in the event your solar array stops producing power.

In recent years, installing solar panels on houses and companies of different sorts has become essential to reduce the ever-increasing cost of gas and electricity. Solar panels can convert sunlight into energy, which can then be used to power homes and businesses. This shift has taken place throughout the most recent years.

Even though installing solar panels is a relatively basic process, this task needs to be carried out by a qualified expert with experience and education in the relevant field. The typical installation of solar panels on a home property may be finished in two to three days. Still, installations on commercial and industrial properties require significantly more time. The most important factors in determining the length of this time difference are the space constraints and the kind of solar panel used.

Before the panels are placed, a group of knowledgeable individuals will examine the property to decide which components are optimal for you and which framework system is necessary for your roof. Then, on the same day your solar panels are being mounted, an aluminum frame system custom-made for your home will also be erected on your roof, complete with steel brackets. If you follow these steps, you can be assured that the location where you keep your solar panels will be safe and sound.

After that, several cables that run behind the installation and are hidden from view are used to secure the panels to the bracket and frame. This is the last step. A qualified electrician can take as much energy from the sun as you need directly if you have your solar panels professionally wired into your home's electrical system.

An inverter will be installed when they have completed the connection to the fuse box in your house. The PV inverter, also known as a solar inverter, is an essential component of the system because it changes the direct current (DC) power made by the solar panels into alternating current (AC), which can be used for various utilities and then if there is any excess, sent back into the larger national grid. Inverters have a lifetime of more than five years. To get the most out of solar panels, you need periodically change them. The last step is the connecting stage, which marks the end of the installation procedure and is followed by testing and commissioning.

The very best installers of solar panels

Either you have already decided to install a solar power system, or you are prepared to start looking for a solar power installation company with a good reputation. Because I know how difficult it may be for you to track down the appropriate installer, I have written a short chapter describing all available choices.

Suppose you are interested in having solar panels placed in your neighborhood. In that case, I believe there are primarily three paths you may take to make that happen. It would seem, given the facts presented here, that

If you know someone who has already had solar panels installed, asking them for references to reliable solar panel installers is an excellent place to start. This might refer to acquaintances such as friends, family, or even neighbors. It's possible that the people who will be doing the installation can answer any of your questions about it and their overall experience working with that installer. They will have responses ready for each question you present to them.

The path that has the least amount of obstacles

You can also use the internet to search for local businesses that are experts in installing solar panels. You may locate anything online using a search engine and enter a keyword or phrase. The search engine will then reappearance a list of results pertinent to your search. There is a good chance that the search results will include listings for solar installation firms that may be found in regional directories. You can learn all you need about the installation from these listings. By glancing at the comments area, you can also see what other people say about the installer and their experiences using it.

No one you know directly or in your immediate family will have any clue whom to advise as a professional installer.

You may now use comparison sites to save time and work by having the installers located for you automatically. Your only input will be your name and an indication of the sort of arrangement you would want, and the company will handle everything else. After collecting all your essential information, they will go through their database to locate a suitable installation.

Any contractor shown on a website of this sort has previously been proven to have the necessary experience level by completing a comprehensive test established for that purpose. Hopefully, the situation with your installers is resolved at this point. However, curiosity drives people to desire to know.

It is in your best attention to look into each of the installers on the list you have gathered, whether you did so via the internet or through the recommendations of friends and family. First, check their website to see if they have samples of their most recent work or comments from clientele who are happy with their services. Then, after you have narrowed down your choices, contact the companies whose services you are most interested in to get price estimates from them. The system that will be the greatest match for you and your property will be detailed in the proposal, along with the facts, ideas, and costs associated with installing it.

CHAPTER 13

Choosing the right battery for your solar power system

Solar battery storage systems are a fantastic alternative to consider. You won't be able to store any energy your system generates for use at an advanced period if you don't have a battery bank. Suppose there is an interruption in the energy provided by the electric grid. In that case, you will not have any other power source available if you do not have a battery. If you attempt to live apart from the rest of society, you will find that your system does not function properly.

Keeping a supply of freshly charged batteries handy can ensure that your electronic gadgets continue functioning as intended. When determining which battery is suitable for your solar panels, you need to consider several factors, including the size of the battery, the amount of power it provides, how efficient it is, and how much it costs. Let's look at the inner workings of solar batteries, the plethora of available alternatives, and my top recommendations so that you can make an educated decision.

How exactly does one go about making a solar power system?

Install a solar battery in conjunction with your solar panels. You will be able to store any excess solar power you generate rather than feed it back into the grid when it is no longer needed. It is expected that you will be able to charge your battery to its maximum capacity with the extra power generated by your solar panels.

Even when a solar energy system is not actively producing electricity, the energy stored in the system may still be used. After the battery has been fully charged, power is sent back into the grid. However, the plug is pulled out of the wall when the power is no longer available.

How many different kinds of batteries are there to choose from?

Batteries that use lead-acid and lithium-ion are the two most popular types of energy storage systems. However, before selecting the kind of battery that will work best for your solar system, you should educate yourself on all available options. There are many numerous kinds of batteries available for purchase today. This chapter will compare lithium-ion batteries to lead-acid batteries and highlight some of the most significant differences between the two types of batteries.

Batteries that are composed completely of li-ion and have reached their maximum capacity. Off-grid solar power systems have used flooded lead-acid (FLA) batteries for over a century. FLA batteries are a kind of deep-cycle battery. When they have fulfilled their function, these batteries may be recycled to a significant degree; the disposal of them does not incur a high financial cost, and doing so is quick and easy.

These are the most effective batteries for solar power, and you should get them if you don't lack to dedicate a lot of cash to keep a check on things. The technology behind batteries has progressed to the point that they can now withstand the daily charge cycles required to remain operational. However, gas production is an unavoidable by-product of their process; hence, adequate ventilation is necessary.

FLA batteries are the way to go if you place a higher priority than anything else on the ability to personalize your setup. Unfortunately, although they are the least expensive alternative, they need maintenance on a more regular basis.

Maintenance is necessary consistently to ensure the continued functionality of these batteries. The fact that the battery must have all its plates submerged in water for the device to function is where the term "floating battery" comes from. To ensure that the plates are always submerged in water, water should be added at predetermined intervals of one month to three months. A good rule of thumb is to do it once a month.

Refillable options are available for lithium-ion battery packs

Suppose you are unable to do routine maintenance on your solar panels. In that case, your best option for powering your system is to use a lead-acid battery that has been sealed.

Because these batteries won't leak and won't do any damage, you may use them without worrying about your safety anyplace you go. Gel and AGM (absorbent glass mat) batteries are two alternative types of sealed lead-acid batteries. Both of these types of batteries have several characteristics in common. The absorbent glass mat is meant to be abbreviated when written as "AGM."

A system that functions without needing any additional external power source is a sealed battery system. In contrast to flooded batteries, there is no need to add water while using them. This implies that they are useful for houses that aren't occupied continually, such as a distant cottage that you visit once or twice a year. One example of this kind of housing is a vacation home. One such example would be purchasing a second home.

Batteries that have been hermetically sealed may be able to resist greater fluctuations in temperature than their non-sealed equivalents. However, suppose you leave them alone for a lengthy period. In that case, you will notice a significant slowdown in the rate at which they free themselves.

Since lithium batteries did not become commercially available in large quantities until the 1970s, their development represents a relatively recent triumph in technology. Their popularity in renewable energy has lately soared, even though they have been present for a considerable time. Even though their prices have increased, the benefits of using lithium batteries continue to outweigh their drawbacks by a significant margin.

- Increase in the likelihood that one will live longer than expected
- No maintenance is required
- Enhancements to the effectiveness of the use of electrical power.
- Air circulation and off-gassing will not be supplied in this environment.

Comparisons of solar batteries may be made in terms of capacity, depth of discharge (DoD), round-trip efficiency (RTE), and battery life, which can assist you in selecting the solar battery that is most suitable for the configuration of your system.

The amount of energy stored in a solar battery is the benchmark used to calculate the standard's capacity for that battery. Kilowatt-hours are the units of measurement for electricity of this kind (kWh).

Using the depth of discharge (DoD) statistic, it is possible to determine what percentage of your battery's total capacity has already been used by your device. If there is a larger need for discharge, the higher capacity for discharge that the battery has will be put to use. The discharge depth should be at least 40% since this is suggested.

To put it another way, the amount of energy it can access is directly proportional to the amount of power required to charge it. Therefore, compared to other possible outcomes, the amount of money saved by using round-trip increases in proportion to the degree of productivity it can attain. Therefore, during the journey, you should strive to achieve an overall efficiency of 80%.

A warranty is necessary because it assures that the battery will continue to work according to the criteria specified by the manufacturer for a certain amount of time or number of cycles.

CHAPTER 14

Step-by-step process to install a solar power system

Instaling solar panels results in advantages that are not only financially beneficial but also environmentally beneficial. There are two practical options available here: either achieving total independence from the grid or making money by selling excess power back to its sources. Both of these options are viable. However, the price of energy causes significant stress for many people.

Installing solar panels is often not a project undertaken by do-it-yourselves enthusiasts but rather by trained experts. However, supposing you are willing to capitalize the time and effort to educate yourself on installing solar panels. In that case, you may be able to save money by not going the professional route.

At any point during the year, photovoltaic cells may have their installations performe. If you live in a zone that receives a significant amount of snow annually, installing solar panels could be something you want to put off until after the snow has melted. This is something that you might want to consider.

Mounting solar panels on a building's roof surface has become more frequent. Therefore, taking additional precautions and using the appropriate safety equipment to prevent falls is essential when working on a roof. Bring the objects up to the roof cautiously, and stay away from the edge as much as possible while working.

To establish a solar power system most effectively, one must have a strong understanding of electricity. If you do not follow all of the essential safety procedures, installing electrical components might potentially put you in danger.

Instructions

A solar panel is made up of solar photovoltaic cells once they have been constructed. Many components of these panels control the use of solar power.

Solar power is a complicated issue involving many different moving pieces. For example, suppose you are considering installing your solar panels. In that case, you must seek the information of experts in solar energy. They will be able to provide you with the direction you want. In addition, they are an excellent resource to turn to for direction if you have problems deciding between several options for the various aspects of your project. When you hire an independent consultant, on the other hand, they will bring in their team of industry professionals to assist you on critical project decisions. These decisions may have a significant impact on the outcome.

A consultant may be able to put you on the proper route to find particular manufacturers if you are seeking them. Determine whether or not your property is appropriate for installing a solar energy system before you go ahead and install one. Utilize these findings to determine whether or not you have enough space in your yard or on your roof to put solar panels on the ground or whether or not your roof has an ideal area for installing solar panels. There is a possibility that some tree felling or pruning of branches will be necessary. In addition, you may need to upgrade the electrical panel in your home. Find out if you may need to replace your roof shortly, and learn about the many roofing options available.

Pick a size

If your home meets the requirements, you will have the opportunity to choose the functions that the system can perform. The energy created may be utilized for several reasons, including but not limited to the power of some appliances and lights in your house. In addition, it can be sold back to the utility company.

Acquire all authorizations

Make an application to your town for permission to carry out construction. Only in some possible jurisdictions is it necessary to get authorization in a different capacity.

Any job that involves electricity requires permission beforehand. The phases of a project in which the project manager is required to wait for approvals and schedule checks are often the most time-consuming components of any project.

Make the most of the available solar electricity by using it in the most efficient manner possible. The central, state and local administrations use various incentive programs to motivate citizens to engage in more positive behaviors. The federal government has the right to make changes to the incentives it currently provides at any moment. In addition, several organizations may be able to provide you with financial assistance in the form of tax credits, and refunds. Before beginning the demanding exercise, submit an application to be considered for these financial incentives.

Preparation

Solar panel components are often acquired a la carte for reasons of ease as well as the flexibility of certain environmental factors. Therefore, it is recommended that a single order be placed for everything required to ensure that all products will be delivered on time. Each material has its own set of applications and benefits, which are complemented by the other.

Putting together racking devices

Determine the best location for the system on your roof or in your yard by doing the necessary calculations and drawing lines. Then, when putting together the metal shelf, follow the instructions provided by the manufacturer. Using roofing tar or silicone caulk to fill in the spaces between the shingles is one way to ensure the roof is watertight.

Prepare the panels

Install the solar panels on the rack with the clamps that were provided. The next thing that needs to be done is to create connections between each panel and those around it. A heat sink has to be incorporated to get the best possible performance. The heat from the panels is released into the air, which then has to be distributed. The array's overall efficiency increases owing to the inclusion of these components.

Configure the controller

It is the responsibility of the charge controller to ensure that electricity is delivered to the appropriate locations. Once it is switched on, there is a possibility that power will go through the system and be stored in the batteries. Therefore, move it between the solar panels and the battery array.

Include a means to power the system

The solar power produced at your home may be saved in a battery bank and used at a later time, even if the sky is overcast and there is no direct sunlight. In addition, many batteries may provide the same amount of power as one single battery if they are linked in series.

You should use the direct current (DC) produced by your solar panel and stored in your batteries. It is necessary to begin by generating alternating current (AC) from direct current (DC) before it can be used in the process of wiring residential properties (AC). After the batteries and power, the controller has been built. Still, before they are linked to the home, it is possible to achieve this goal by constructing an electrical power inverter.

Installing a power meter

Almost all solar panel installations also include some energy monitoring systems in today's world. This device can monitor the electrical current that is produced and the electrical current that is consumed. As a result, it can monitor the amount of energy being drawn from the grid and the amount being returned to it at any given time.

Before you connect your new solar panel system, you must ensure that the wiring has been checked. Conduct the essential tests to ensure that the grounding of the solar panels is correct.

CHAPTER 15

Configuration of on-grid and off-grid solar power systems

It could be challenging for a customer to install either an on-grid or an off-grid solar power system to estimate the number of solar panels they will need, the amount of energy they will use, and other elements. Even though the photovoltaic (PV) effect is one of the most important aspects of solar power systems, it is ultimately up to the user to decide how the energy generated by solar devices is used. An off-grid solar panel system is likely the most suitable choice if you want to use solar energy but would prefer not to depend on the public electrical grid.

It is not difficult to distinguish between solar systems linked to the grid and those not connected to the grid. A solar system that is linked to the utility grid is referred to as being on-grid. In contrast, a solar system not linked to the utility grid is considered off-grid. The installation cost for each customer is determined by several variables, one of which is the kind of grid system the client opts to use.

To put it in simple terms, a solar power installation hooked into the public electrical grid is called an on-grid system. Since utility providers indemnify consumers if their solar panels don't operate, on-grid systems are more common than off-grid ones. Because of this, grid-connected systems are becoming more desirable to purchasers. For example, suppose a customer creates more electricity than they use. In that case, the utility company may offer to buy it back from them at a discounted cost. In addition, there is an option that the customer's actions may result in a credit that will be available for usage at the end of the billing cycle.

Because the customer won't need to purchase a battery backup device, the initial investment required to connect to the grid will be lower for them. One of the most significant drawbacks of using a system connected to the grid is that it will become completely inoperable if there is a disruption in the power supply. This indicates that an on-grid power system may not be able to generate sufficient output in locations that often experience disruptions to the utility power supply.

A backup battery pack is the energy source for a solar power system that is not connected to the grid. This is because the infrastructure is not connected to the general public's source of electricity. The capacity of an off-grid system to store the electricity generated throughout the day in batteries so that it may be used later is one of the system's most important advantages. You can still use the energy stored in the batteries even when the weather outside is cloudy or night-time. If off-grid solar power choices can fulfill the user's energy requirements, then the user may decide to go with such options.

According to the findings of the energy estimations, solar power systems have the potential to be increased to deliver sufficient amounts of electricity around the clock, seven days a week. Users of off-grid solar panels do not risk themselves during a power outage since these panels do not depend on the conventional electrical system. Because the amount of energy produced by off-grid solar systems is highly dependent on the amount of solar radiation received, prolonged periods of gloomy weather may significantly impact the amount of power generated. It's possible that installing a second battery system may result in a large increase in the total cost of the original installation.

A solar power system of this kind has to be linked directly to the utility grid for you to be able to use the energy for your typical activities. It is the tactic that is used the majority of the time in houses all around the world. The houses will not sustain any damage under all circumstances, regardless of whether there is an abundance or deficiency of energy. Even in its most basic configuration, an on-grid system can accommodate varying power supplies and does not jeopardize its functioning.

Another essential component of this system is called "net metering," It gives users the ability to store excess energy in the grid in return for credit that may be utilized whenever they choose. Again, it is not difficult to see the rationale for the widespread adoption of this practice.

If you use this plan, it won't be essential to purchase an expensive power-saving battery for a system connected to the grid, which will reduce the overall cost of the system.

If the user is acquainted with the path energy takes from the central power grid to individual households, installing and operating an on-grid solar system is a straightforward and uncomplicated process without discomfort. The following is a concise overview of the procedure that must be followed.

The power travels from a connected source to the residence of a customer. It is then returned to the grid after being used. This is the feature that differentiates this system from others, and it is also why it is one of the possibilities that may be both versatile and helpful.

Solar panels installed on rooftops may be wired directly into the user's house's electrical system or the surrounding area's power grid. Solar energy is converted into usable electricity via a technique known as direct current.

After being changed from direct current (DC) to alternating current (AC) by an inverter, the energy may be utilized for anything that a regular home circuit would ordinarily power. In addition, the operation of the air conditioner results in the flow of energy back into the grid; this helps to ensure that there is no disruption in the power supply to the house.

Additionally, the inverter maintains a consistent power supply throughout your home. This may place if the power supply is more than what is required by the house. Clienteles will be billed once a month for the amount of energy recorded by their net meters as a direct consequence of this change.

Being "off-grid" means that you do not have a direct connection to the electrical grid or the local utility company. This might also mean that you do not get electricity from the grid. This is how the phrase is often understood when used.

This alternative is not dependent on the electrical grid maintained by the utility company in the same way that conventional on-grid systems are. You may be able to get all of the energy you need from an independent power source. However, in contrast to systems linked to a grid, it does not deliver all of the benefits that those other systems provide. The most significant impact on the budget will be caused by the purchase of an extra battery system to store any excess energy. Solar energy has the possibility to be a sustainable energy source, yet, many people have been put off by the fact that the required equipment is both expensive and difficult to move. This has caused a significant barrier to entry for solar energy.

Solar panels are installed to generate electricity used inside the house. Any excess is saved in batteries for later use. This equipment is essential in remote locations that are cut off from main power grids because of their location. Because of their backup system, the flow of energy will not be disrupted, and it will continue to be produced throughout the year, regardless of how bad the weather may get.

After being created and stored in batteries, energy is transported to the home, where it is used to power various appliances, including but not limited to the lights and the refrigerator. The electricity is sent to various parts of the house through an intricate system that consists of cables and outlets.

When sunshine shines on a solar panel, it triggers a chain of chemical reactions that results in energy production. This power is then sent to the system's batteries for storage. As long as there is a consistent flow of electricity into the system, the batteries will continue to charge even if the power may fluctuate. The house will continue to get power directly from the batteries for as long as the current charge is maintained.

CHAPTER 16

Best practices to maintain the solar power system

B efore you hire someone to undertake maintenance work, here are some of the most fundamental tips you should follow.

Due to the inherent ability of solar panels to do their maintenance, there is never a risk that they will become ineffective or stop working properly. In most cases, cleaning is the only kind of required panel maintenance. However, dirt may accumulate on your solar panels if you live in an area that experiences extreme weather or has long periods of dryness. Maintaining the cleanliness of solar panels allows them to absorb the most sunlight possible; thus, this activity should be performed consistently.

In addition, you are strongly advised to inspect your solar panels at least once a year. Once your solar panels have been mounted on your roof, the company that installed them should, as a matter of course, send a professional to check them over. This is the standard operating procedure.

When you become aware that there is a problem with your solar panels or when you see that they are not producing as much power as they are capable of, schedule appointments for maintenance to be performed on them. Solar panels, as was just said, are low-maintenance. So, to sum up, there are three-time frames that must be considered.

If you want to get the most out of your solar panels, it's a good idea to have a professional look at them once a year, if not more often.

A least twice per year is optional for cleaning solar panels. You may only need to clean your solar panels once a year if you live in a rainy climate and they don't accumulate much dirt. This is very important if you are in an area that obtains a great deal of sunlight. However, if you live in a dry setting or an area that receives little rain, or if dirt and wreckage tend to build up on your solar panels, you may want to factor in the additional expenses associated with cleaning them more often.

Aside from the routine inspections and cleanings you give your solar panel system, it should need very little maintenance. However, there are scarce red flags you should watch out for that might mean your panels will need repair sooner than you thought.

Suppose you observe a decrease in the quantity of electricity that your solar panels generate. In that case, getting them inspected as soon as possible is essential. On the other hand, suppose you see a rise in your monthly power bill and a considerable drop in the amount of energy your solar panels produce. In that case, this is a warning sign that your solar panels need maintenance and should be serviced as soon as it is practical.

The expense associated with maintaining solar panels

Once a year, a professional should clean and examine the solar panels to ensure they are functioning properly. Because there are so many solar panels on the roof, it is necessary to work with an experienced installation. Even when handled by a trained expert, routine property maintenance costs are reasonable and not prohibitive.

According to Home Advisor's calculations, the cost of maintaining solar panels every year might range anywhere from $150 to $300. The price of the annual inspection is $150, and the cost of the two cleanings is similarly $150. Suppose components of your solar panel system fail or dirt and debris build up on the panels faster than usual. In that case, this might increase the costs of the system's maintenance.

How much you save on repairs and maintenance for your solar panels depends on how well they were installed.

The manufacturer of your solar panels will provide a warranty that specifies how long you can expect those panels to continue functioning under typical circumstances. Although most warranties are good for between 10 and 20 years, a few are good for up to 25 years. These warranties assure, first and foremost, that the performance of your solar panels will not fall below the standard that has been agreed upon. In addition, they protect your solar panels against damage you did not cause, such as that caused by hurricanes or other natural catastrophes. This safeguards that your asset is not wasted.

Remember that the warranty on your solar panels may only be valid if you do routine maintenance on them as specified in the manual. For example, suppose you don't maintain your solar panels clean. In that case, their warranty might end up being voided before it's even up for renewal.

The cost of solar panels may be comparable to that of other everyday goods and necessities. In addition, keeping them in good status is much simpler, and they may be used for a much longer period than their predecessors. Therefore, the only true need for annual maintenance of your solar panels is to check them and stretch them good housework once a year. As long as you maintain your panels in excellent condition throughout the year, you won't have to do further maintenance.

What kind of damage may bad weather potentially cause?

The durability of solar panels was one of the most important factors taken into account during their creation. Therefore, solar panels need to be placed by the most stringent guidelines to endure even the most adverse conditions.

As a result, the Department of Energy of the United States concluded that solar panels could withstand hail. In addition, solar panels are resilient, as shown by the fact that Hurricane Florence in 2018 caused little to no damage to those installed in North Carolina.

They might sustain damage from hail, a hurricane, a tornado, or even a lightning strike. If the device you purchased comes with a warranty, any damaged panels may be repaired or replaced at your discretion.

On the other hand, it is often the hot weather that is the cause of problems with solar panels. Solar panels experience a loss of around one percent of their efficiency for every degree Fahrenheit over 77 (or 25 degrees Celsius).

By inspiring them a few ins above the ground or the ceiling, air can flow around them, which helps to keep them cool and ensures that they will continue to generate energy for an unlimited amount of time. As a direct result of this, the air can circulate all the way freely around them. Even if the temperature increases, there is no need to be concerned about the effectiveness of your solar panels since your installation will adjust to the weather trends in your area.

Repairing and upgrading your solar panels

When it comes to repairing or replacing panels, your best choice is to hire a professional to do the work for you.

Suppose you observe a loss in performance while a warranty still covers your solar panels. In that case, it is essential to interact with the company that installed your solar panels as soon as possible. If the problem cannot be resolved, a maintenance specialist will be sent, and new panels will be put in place.

The manufacturer's warranty on one of your unconnected pieces of equipment may cover the damage to your panels. With the assistance of your solar panel installer, you should be able to find a firm that can provide you with new solar panels to replace the outdated ones you already have. Do not attempt to install or repair solar panels on your own if you lack understanding about the installation and maintenance of home solar systems. This includes both the installation and maintenance of solar panels.

Warranties for solar panels may cover all of the most prevalent issues.

When your solar panel is covered by its warranty, the company who installed it will replace it with a new one at no extra cost. It is suggested that solar panels have a warranty that covers at least 80% of their energy output for the first 15–25 years of their life. This will ensure that you get the most out of your investment.

CHAPTER 17

Most common mistakes and how to avoid them

T he amount of power accessible to you before the system's installation was enough. Your capability to produce electricity will need to be increased at some point. You've likely just welcomed some new roommates into your home or splurged on the newest Tesla Cyber Truck model or cutting-edge gadget.

Unfortunately, how things are set up now cannot accommodate your requirements. You can decide to install new solar panels if the electricity produced by the ones you already have on your roof is inadequate. You may want to consider increasing the output of your system if the number of electrical kilowatts it generates is now lower than what you need.

- You can consider investing in solar panels that have improved photovoltaic conversion efficiencies as an alternative.
- Before beginning production, it is essential to determine how much you will need, the dimensions of your roof, and your financial constraints.
- Is your solar power system possibly providing all the energy you require?
- There is a considerable likelihood that your energy requirements are more than what can be provided by your solar panels. Therefore, instructions that are easy to comprehend must be included in the application and the receipt for the power bill.
- The business installing the solar panels must demonstrate how the system functions under optimal circumstances. Suppose how it is supposed to perform and function are significantly different from one another. In that case, there may be something wrong with your system.
- If you observe any of the following, there may be anything wrong with the functioning of your computer:
- You need to consider the local environment to get the most out of your solar energy system and make it as real as possible. For example, cities that get a significant amount of sunlight have the potential to generate a greater quantity of energy.
- It is laudable to work toward independent energy while also being nice to the environment. However, setting up solar panel systems is not as simple as it may initially seem. Even the slightest bit of carelessness or ignorance might severely impact the effectiveness of solar panels. Therefore, when building a system that uses solar panels, it is essential to keep the following in mind.

Utilizing this checklist is one way to improve the efficiency with which solar panels are installed significantly. It may be likely to increase the efficiency of solar panels to meet certain requirements if they are correctly labeled from the top down. The following is how we would describe them:

Exposing less productive sections of the plant to the sun to absorb some of its rays. When it comes to solar panels, preventing corrosion is as easy as ensuring that all electrical components are installed correctly. Also, keep a close watch on the direction the wind is blowing from since this might cause the wire loops to quiver, resulting in noise and sparks. Finally, by the guidelines for building construction in the area, the material for cable conduit must be stainless steel.

Solar panels are not receiving the appropriate maintenance

In a string setup, each PV system is connected to the one that comes after it. If you look prudently sufficient, you may be astonished at how much of an effect even a small quantity of shadow can have on a single panel. When you compare images of your roof taken at regular intervals, you will be able to determine whether or not it is in excellent shape and whether or not it requires care. If it is impossible to avoid shade, technological solutions like microinverters and DC optimizers may be employed to stop even a single shaded panel from restricting the system's output.

Most consumers buy a solar energy system after reviewing their electric bill and calculating the energy they typically use daily. But unfortunately, this technique does not consider the voltage, the orientation of the panels, and the gradual decrease in efficiency over time.

It's possible that these factors ultimately decide the result of the endeavor. For example, poor voltage maintenance in either your battery bank or your panel can cause the expensive gear to malfunction. The consequences of this act could be catastrophic in the long run. The entire system may be ruined if, for example, the voltage of your solar panels or your battery bank is off.

Ignoring how important it is to check for damages

To begin, you should search for "micro-flaws," often known as extremely small cracks that can only be spotted by carefully examining the item in question. For example, a solar panel may be damaged if it is handled incorrectly or subjected to an excessive amount of force. As the crack worsens, the amount of electricity a solar panel produces will decrease.

Take good care of all the components already in place since this is the most effective approach to prevent rust from forming on the solar panels. It is important to remember that the volume may expand, and electric sparks may be produced due to the wind-driving wire loops back and forth. To comply with the area's fire prevention regulations, cable conduits made of stainless steel are advised.

Using ineffective resources and techniques

Using cheaper inverters and solar panels makes it feasible to save money; however, only a percentage of those savings will be delivered by affordable solar panels that have not been demonstrated to work well. Panels produced by third-party manufacturers are subjected to exhaustive life cycle testing before being sold. Because there is often only space for one inverter in a configuration, dependability is very important. The most significant thing you can do to guarantee that your converter will continue to help you well for a long time is to investigate the warranty term.

Installers are an issue that seldom receives attention

When it comes to the preparation and applying solar energy systems, it is a good indicator if a company has designers and installers on staff who have been awarded certification in the relevant fields. Solar energy systems installed by electricians who do not have valid licenses are ineligible for financial assistance from the government. Find that a registered electrician didn't install your system. It may be difficult and costly to get your money back for it.

Having to maintain a proactive stance concerning power disruptions requires constant vigilance. Even though you don't have to connect your solar panels to the grid to function, you should be aware that if the grid loses electricity, so will your solar panels. If this occurs, the backup batteries for your solar panel system will begin charging. However, because of a fault in the system that integrates electricity, the electronics and lights will continue to operate off the batteries even if there is energy available to power them.

Suppose your home just has the essential appliances and electronics. In that case, all you will need to do to provide it with electricity is connect a solar panel and a backup battery. However, if more attention were given to power integration, problems with the power supply and inefficient use may be avoided.

Things that should be considered before installing solar panels on your home

After utilizing your solar power system for an extended length of time or after electing to invest in the production of more energy, you could decide to upgrade it. Changes, also often referred to as upgrades, are adjustments that are purposefully done to a system to enhance its overall performance. Repairing a system often includes restoring it to the state in which it was found; nevertheless, upgrades might involve altering the system. We have industrialized a list of things to think about to assist you in preparing to install new solar panels or replace existing ones.

Because solar panels are getting less expensive, the amount that you pay for each additional kilowatt-hour may be less than you anticipate. Although it is a reasonable assumption that a bigger solar system will result in lower pricing, there are situations where this is not always the case. There are several circumstances in which this is not the case. To be successful, you must pay careful attention to these guidelines. In addition, maintenance and upgrades are greatly facilitated by markings placed across solar panels.

Utilizing the Solar Monitoring App is, without a doubt, the most effective method for gathering data. Tracking software is used by retailers of solar energy systems to keep tabs on the amount of power consumed by and produced by their consumers. Suppose you read your monthly energy bills carefully. In that case, monitoring any price changes, including hikes and reductions, will be easier. Using an inverter is the simplest and fastest technique to determine the state of your system. If you want to ensure that the results of the calculations are accurate, one option available to you is to enhance your solar power system. The International Electrotechnical Commission (IEC) 62109 standard was updated in 2015 to include a ground fault warning, the purpose of which is to alert the owners of solar systems to any issues that may arise with the grounding.

Write down everything you'll need to complete the project

I would be quite thankful if you might just let me know how many extra solar panels you would be interested in acquiring. Thank you in advance for your assistance. Since the answer to this question will have far-reaching effects on the project's scope and additional expenditures, it is the most critical issue to answer. You would need a solar power system with some wiggle space if you wanted to use the energy generated by a solar panel with a rating of 600 watts to power a large machine. Because the efficiency of a solar panel is only approximately 80%, and it only gets sunlight for a tiny portion of the day, you should proceed with care before depending on it as your primary energy source.

Determine if it is necessary to upgrade your current inverters

Suppose you wish to increase the amount of electricity generated by your system as a whole. In that case, you may need to improve the inverter. You may want a more powerful central inverter if the amount of energy generated by your solar panels is high. Installing a power optimizer or string inverter system is more involved than incorporating a micro-inverter into an already established solar panel system. In general, it is recommended that older, less user-friendly versions be replaced with their counterparts that are more up-to-date and user-friendly. While adjustments are being made to the roof's structure, it is recommended that a miniature inverter be used rather than a conventional inverter. All required to satisfy a need for 6 kW may be adding additional panels to a system with an inverter rated at 5 kW.

Use extreme caution during the entire process

You may lose your present feed-in tariffs if you upgrade your solar panels. If the extra solar panels are considered a new system, then the prices will remain the same as they are now. However, the installation of such a system would need significant financial investment.

However, solar energy systems have several limitations on their size and significant expenses connected with their installation. The system's theoretical maximum capacity may be considered adequate for certain applications. In other circumstances, however, you are not restricted in any way in your ability to choose the available bandwidth. In addition, the expense of conducting a "network study" may need to be covered to ascertain your system's influence on the network's voltage and distortion levels. There are certain suppliers of electricity grids that impose this price.

Do not try to use pieces that are incompatible with each other

To ensure that the scheme lasts to function correctly, any additional panels connected in series or parallel to the inverter of an already-existing system must have the same or greater wattage. This is required for the inverter to function correctly and manage the extra power. However, suppose their manufacturer's warranty still covers the pre-existing solar panels and inverters and is in outstanding condition or in good working order. In that case, creating a new system that uses just those components may be possible. In addition, because each panel has its inverter and can be positioned in any direction, these inverters provide more flexibility than typical string inverters when there is partial shading.

4 important tips

The adoption rate of solar panels has increased dramatically since the government began providing rebates and tax credits for their use. So why not put something on your roof that reduces your energy bills and saves you money in the long run?

Although the unpackaged of your effort will be done once your panels are operational, there is still more to do. For example, regular maintenance and inspections are still necessary if you want to get the most out of your solar panels. In this final chapter, readers will find four tips for maximizing solar panels' productivity.

Solar panels should be cleaned regularly

Avoid making cleaning your solar panels a regular part of your schedule, but do it at least twice a year. Water and cloth made of microfiber are all that you will need to clean it effectively. Contrarily, suppose your photovoltaic panels are roof-mounted. In that case, you should never try to do this yourself; instead, contact a seasoned solar panel installation.

You should get a battery to store the energy

A battery system, which stores any surplus energy generated by solar panels, is an absolute must if you don't already have one. Because of this, you may keep using your solar panels for a good amount of the night without connecting to the grid. While the sun is out and providing power, a separate battery system might be used to store energy for use when clouds cover the sky.

If you want to know what kind of battery system is recommended, you should get in touch with the firm that puts in your solar panels. Many jurisdictions provide rebates for acquiring solar batteries, notwithstanding their high cost.

Make the most of the day

When the sun is up, you can use renewable energy to power your home indefinitely without spending a dime. If this describes your desire, you should take advantage of daylight hours as much as possible to do chores like the weekly laundry, electronic device charging, and daily bathing.

By shifting your energy usage to the mornings instead of the evenings, you may reduce your monthly energy costs and help ease the strain on the power grid.

If you want to maximize the output of your solar panels, you still need to monitor your daily energy use. Your home's energy needs may exceed the quantity of electricity produced by your solar panels. Connecting to the power grid is required to store the surplus energy. Do not use several appliances at once; wait for each to complete its cycle before going on to the next.

Cut down the overgrown bushes

Solar panel owners discovering that some of their panels are no longer getting enough sunshine must determine what is blocking the light. There is a clear indication that lengthy exposure to shade may reduce solar panel efficiency and cause a string inverter to fail. Furthermore, a tree should have its branches trimmed down if it blocks the view.

While moving a building blocking the sun may not be possible, a microinverter or DC power optimizer may be used to increase the efficiency of the panels that are not in the shadow. This will help you to get the most out of solar panels.

Lightning Source UK Ltd.
Milton Keynes UK
UKHW010816090223
416681UK00002B/460